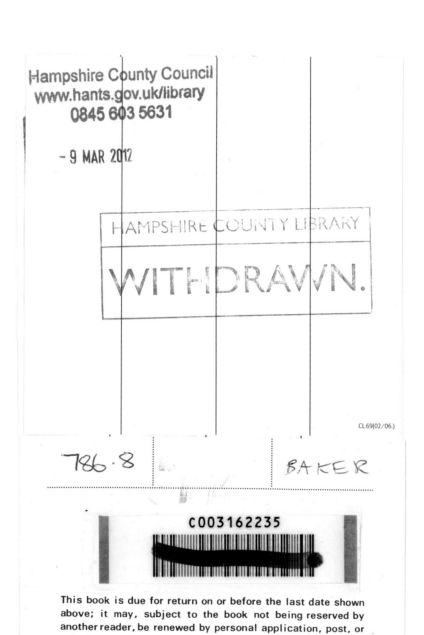

HOME ORGANIST LIBRARY VOLUME 21

War Songs

Arranged by Kenneth Baker.

Wise Publications
London/New York/Paris/Sydney/Copenhagen/Madrid

Exclusive Distributors:
Music Sales Limited
8/9 Frith Street, London W1V 5TZ, England.
Music Sales Pty Limited
120 Rothschild Avenue, Rosebery, NSW 2018, Australia.

Order No. AM92368
ISBN 0-7119-4444-X
This book © Copyright 1994 by Wise Publications

Book design by Studio Twenty, London
Computer management by Adam Hay Editorial Design
Compiled by Peter Evans
Music arranged by Kenneth Baker
Music processed by MSS Studios
Cover photograph by Hulton Deutsch

Printed in the United Kingdom by
J.B. Offset Printers (Marks Tey) Limited, Marks Tey, Essex.

Your Guarantee of Quality
As publishers, we strive to produce every book to
the highest commercial standards.
The music has been freshly engraved and the book has
been carefully designed to minimise awkward page turns
and to make playing from it a real pleasure.
Particular care has been given to specifying acid-free, neutral-sized
paper made from pulps which have not been elemental chlorine bleached.
This pulp is from farmed sustainable forests and
was produced with special regard for the environment.
Throughout, the printing and binding have been planned to ensure a
sturdy, attractive publication which should give years of enjoyment.
If your copy fails to meet our high standards, please inform us
and we will gladly replace it.
Music Sales' complete catalogue describes thousands of titles and is
available in full colour sections by subject, direct from Music Sales Limited.
Please state your areas of interest and send a cheque/postal order
for £1.50 for postage to: Music Sales Limited, Newmarket Road,
Bury St. Edmunds, Suffolk IP33 3YB.

Mister Brown Of London Town

Words & Music by R. Arkell & Noel Gay.

Upper: saxophone
Lower: flutes + piano
Pedal: 16' + 8'
Drums: swing

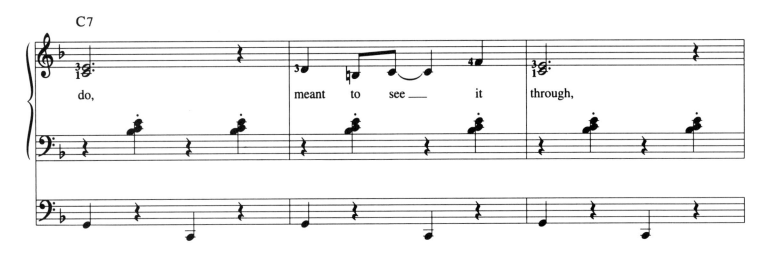

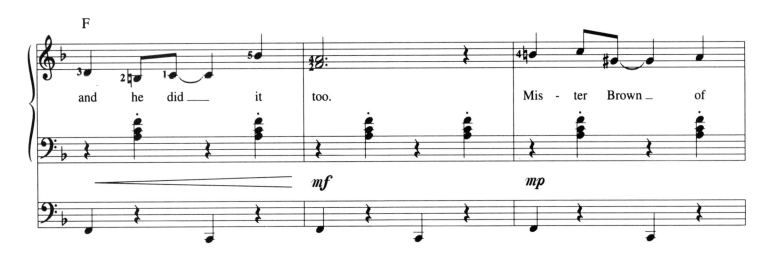

4

I'll Never Smile Again, Until I Smile At You

Words & Music by Ruth Lowe.

Upper: guitar
Lower: flutes
Pedal: 8'
Drums: swing

In The Quartermaster's Stores
(My Eyes Are Dim)

Words & Music Adapted by Elton Box, Desmond Cox & Bert Reed.

Upper: trumpet
Lower: flutes + piano
Pedal: bass guitar
Drums: swing

11

5. There is beer, beer,
    Beer you can't get near,
    In the stores, in the stores.
    There is rum, rum,
    For the General's tum,
    In the Quartermaster's stores.
        My eyes are dim (etc.)

6. There was cake, cake,
    Cake you couldn't break,
    In the stores, in the stores.
    There were flies, flies,
    Feeding on the pies,
    In the Quartermaster's stores.
        My eyes are dim (etc.)

When They Sound The Last All Clear

Words & Music by Hugh Charles & Louis Elton.

Upper: trumpet
Lower: flutes
Pedal: 8'
Drums: waltz

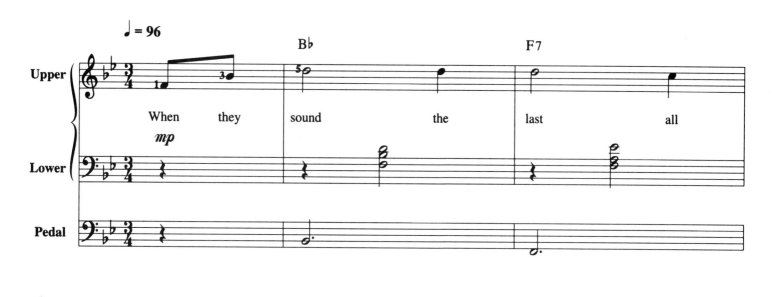

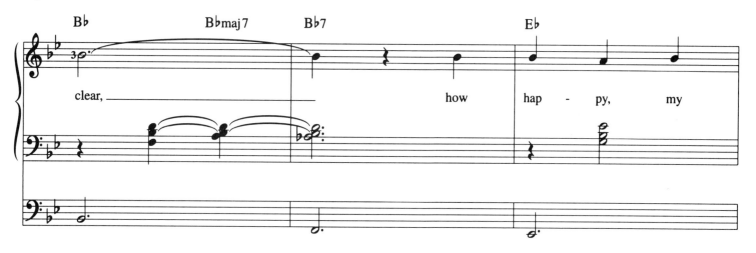

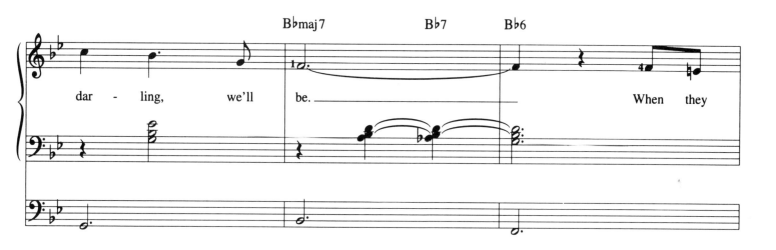

Run, Rabbit, Run

Music by Noel Gay. Words by Noel Gay & Ralph Butler.

Upper: brass ensemble
Lower: flutes + piano
Pedal: 8'
Drums: swing

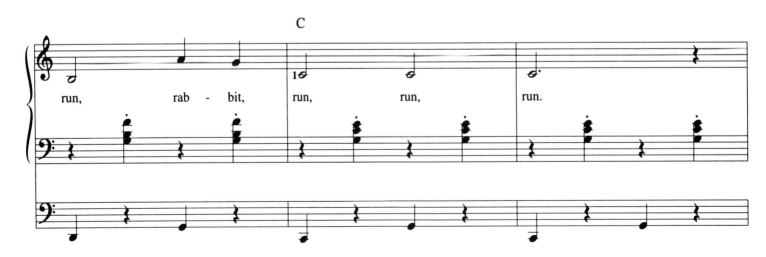

Don't give the far - - - mer his fun, fun,

fun. He'll get by with -

out his rab - bit pie, so run, rab - bit,

run, rab - bit, run, run, run!

(pedal gliss.)

↑ stop drums

Praise The Lord And Pass The Ammunition

Words & Music by Frank Loesser.

Upper: saxophone
Lower: flutes
Pedal: 16' + 8'
Drums: off (VERSE) swing (CHORUS)

Falling In Love Again

Music & Original Words by Friedrich Hollander. English Words by Reg Connelly.

Upper: guitar
Lower: flutes
Pedal: 16' + 8'
Drums: waltz

Hey, Little Hen

Words & Music by Ralph Butler & Noel Gay.

Upper: trombone
Lower: flutes + piano
Pedal: 8'
Drums: swing

The Homecoming Waltz

Words & Music by Bob Musel, Ray Sonin & Reg Connelly.

Upper: accordion
Lower: flute
Pedal: 16' + 8'
Drums: waltz

There's Something About A Soldier

Words & Music by Noel Gay.

Upper: trumpet
Lower: flutes + piano
Pedal: 16' + 8'
Drums: march 2/4 (or 4/4)

may be a great big gen - 'ral, may be a ser - geant

ma - jor, may be a sim - ple pri - vate of the

cresc.

line, line, line. But there's some - thing a - bout his

f   *mf*

bea - ring, some - thing in what he's wea - ring,

When The Lights Go On Again
(All Over The World)

Words & Music by Eddie Seiler, Sol Marcus & Bennie Benjemen.

Upper: violin
Lower: flutes
Pedal: 8'
Drums: swing

The Fleet's In Port Again

Words & Music by Noel Gay.

Upper: flute + clarinet
Lower: flutes + piano
Pedal: 16' + 8'
Drums: swing

Whispering Grass

Words by Fred Fisher. Music by Doris Fisher.

Upper: vibraphone
Lower: flutes
Pedal: 16' + 8'
Drums: swing

Why do you whis-per green grass? Why tell the trees what ain't so?

Whis-per-ing grass, — the trees don't need — to know, —

no, no. — Why tell them all your

Upper: to vibraphone

told them once be - fore, now it's no se - cret a - ny more. Why tell them all the old things? They're bu - ried un - der the snow, whis - per - ing grass, don't tell the trees, 'cause the trees don't need to know.

↑ stop drums

There'll Always Be An England

Words & Music by Ross Parker & Hughie Charles.

Upper: trumpet
Lower: flutes + piano
Pedal: 16' + 8'
Drums: march 2/4 (or 4/4)

Goodnight, Wherever You Are

Words & Music by Dick Robertson, Al Hoffman & Frank Weldon.

Upper: muted trumpet
Lower: flutes
Pedal: 8'
Drums: latin

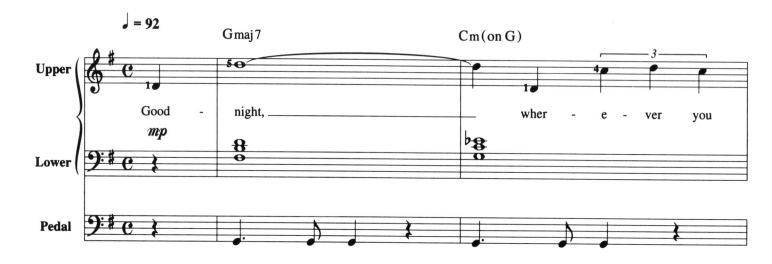

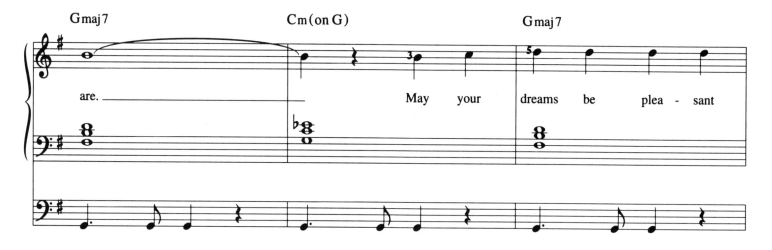

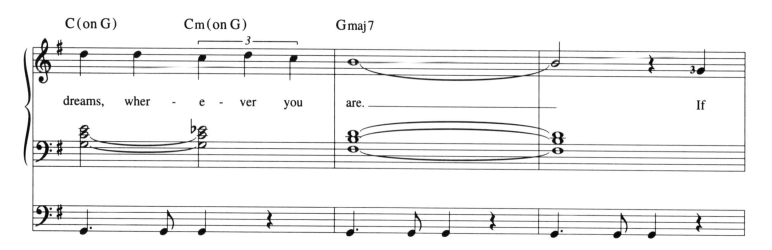

48

You Are My Sunshine

Words & Music by Jimmie Davis & Charles Mitchell.

Upper: clarinet
Lower: flutes
Pedal: 8'
Drums: swing

stop drums

51

All Over The Place

Words by Noel Gay & Frank Eyton. Music by Noel Gay.

Upper: piano
Lower: flute
Pedal: 8'
Drums: swing

54

Boogie Woogie Bugle Boy

Words & Music by Don Raye & Hughie Prince.

Upper: jazz guitar + trumpet
Lower: piano
Pedal: bass guitar
Drums: 8 beat (or rock)

Bless You (For Being An Angel)

Words & Music by Eddie Lane & Don Baker.

Upper: flute
Lower: flutes + piano
Pedal: 16' + 8'
Drums: swing

I'm Thinking Tonight Of My Blue Eyes

Words & Music by A.P. Carter.

Upper: accordion
Lower: flutes
Pedal: 16' + 8'
Drums: swing

Silver Wings In The Moonlight

Music by Sonny Miller & Leo Towers. Words by Hugh Charles.

Upper: piano
Lower: flutes
Pedal: 8'
Drums: swing

Let The People Sing

Words by Noel Gay, Ian Grant & Frank Eyton. Music by Noel Gay.

Upper: trumpet
Lower: flutes + piano
Pedal: 16' + 8'
Drums: swing

Cleanin' My Rifle (And Dreamin' Of You)

Words & Music by Wrubel.

Upper: piano
Lower: flutes
Pedal: 8'
Drums: swing

Always In My Heart

Words by Kim Gannon. Music by Ernesto Lecuona.

Upper: flute
Lower: flutes + piano
Pedal: 8'
Drums: beguine (or latin)

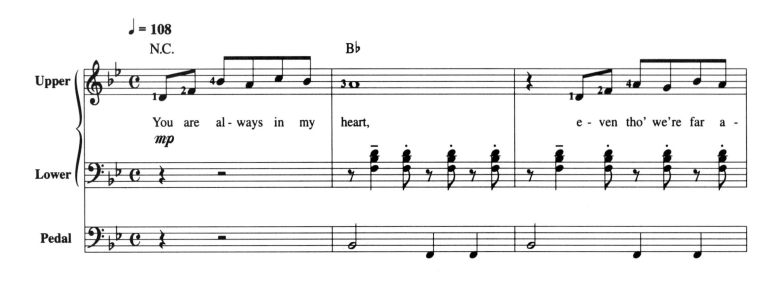

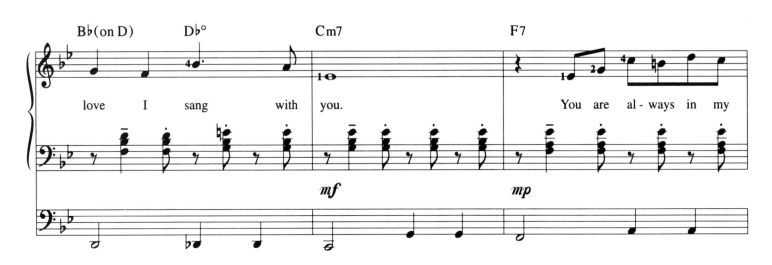

Goodnight Sweetheart

Words & Music by Ray Noble, Jimmy Campbell & Reg Connelly.

Upper: brass ensemble
Lower: flutes + piano
Pedal: 16' + 8'
Drums: swing

We'll Meet Again

Words & Music by Ross Parker & Hughie Charles.

Upper: guitar
Lower: flutes
Pedal: 16' + 8'
Drums: swing